This Mutts Be LOVE!

A Binky and Bell Coloring Book

By Rick Gardner and Eilish Boyd

Dedicated to all of volunteers, staff, and donors who make all the rescues and shelters of the world happen. Thank you for all the passion, service, and love you bring to homeless pets every day!
— Rick and Eilish

Printed in the United States of America

ISBN 978-1-956543-14-8

Book design and layout by Eilish Boyd
Cover design/graphic art by Eilish Boyd
Illustrations © by Binky and Bell

www.writewaypublishing.com

WRITEWAY PUBLISHING

Thank you for supporting homeless pets through your purchase of this book. Binky and Bell's mission is to support these pets in rescues and shelters by the sale of our artwork and through fundraising endeavors. This book is one of our endeavors.

Dogs are our comfort and joy. They make us happy. We hope that you enjoy these drawings and that they create a ray of sunshine, love, and happiness in your day. Enjoy!

Rick Gardner
Binky and Bell

P.S. If you enjoyed this book, consider purchasing a copy for a friend!

This book comes with more free pages! Visit binkyandbell.com to download yours today!

Your purchase of this book benefits two Raleigh, NC, area rescues: Friends of Wake County Animal Shelter and Freedom Ride Rescue.

Friends of Wake County Animal Center

www.friendsofwakeanimals.org

Friends of Wake County Animal Center, also known as FWCAC, is dedicated to improving the quality of life for animals and their human families in the Wake County, North Carolina community. Through fundraising efforts, FWCAC provides access to vital medical care, boarding, and placement for shelter animals in need, thereby improving their health and reducing euthanasia rates at the center. The FWCAC team promotes adoption, safety, and responsible pet ownership via education and public outreach. Finally, FWCAC provides support to local rescues, animal shelters, and adopters to help diminish the number of homeless animals.

Freedom Ride Rescue

www.freedom-ride.org

Freedom Ride Rescue is proud to be the crazy dog lovers who skip out on work to transport dogs from all over the state to their excited fosters' homes, who stay up late searching shelter pages for that next "Freedom Ride" potential, and who volunteer countless hours making rescue a reality.

Freedom Ride Rescue is run by volunteers. They are foster-based; they have no facility; and every one of their adoptable (and not-quite-ready-to-be-adopted) animals are in homes where families are teaching trust, love, and basic manners—preparing dogs to be the best addition to a family that they can be.

Their fosters have had their hearts broken after they love, rehabilitate, and nurse an unwanted, unloved animal until it prances away with their fur-ever person (often never looking back) and start their life's most wonderful chapter: the one as a cherished pet.

Freedom Ride Rescue is a wonderful, tight-knit family needing volunteers, fosters, donors, and people willing to care.

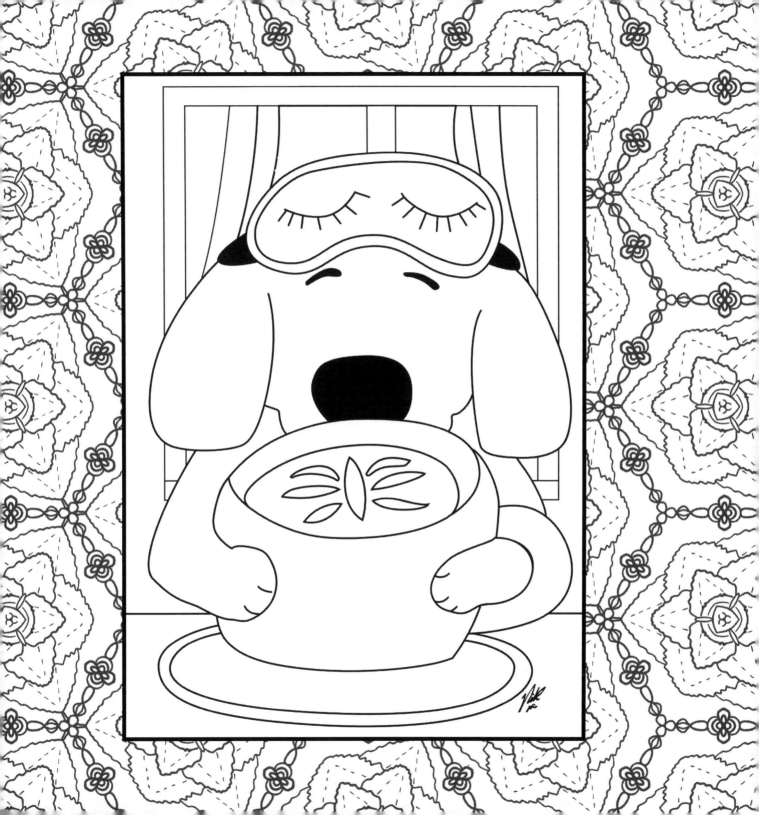

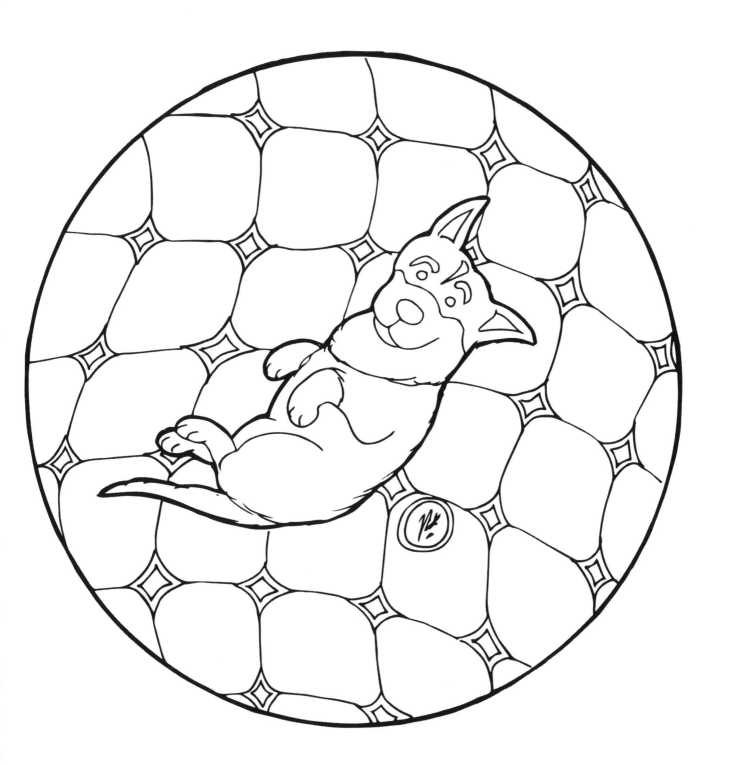

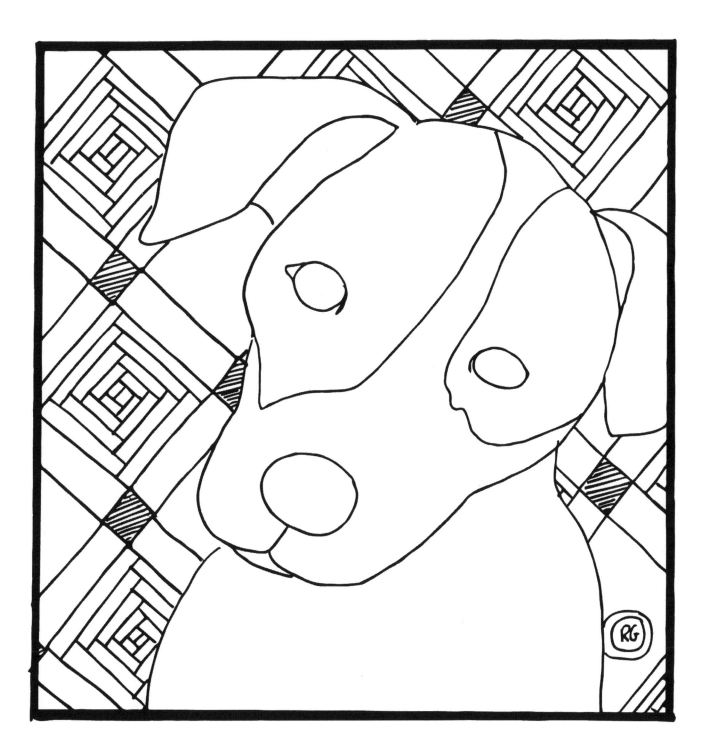

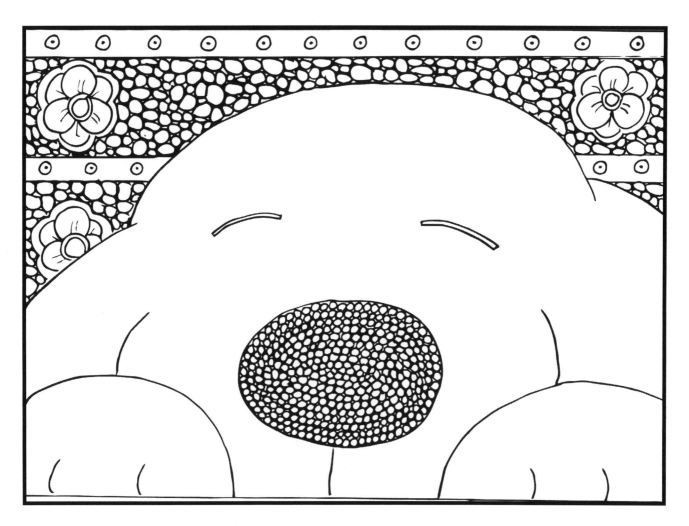

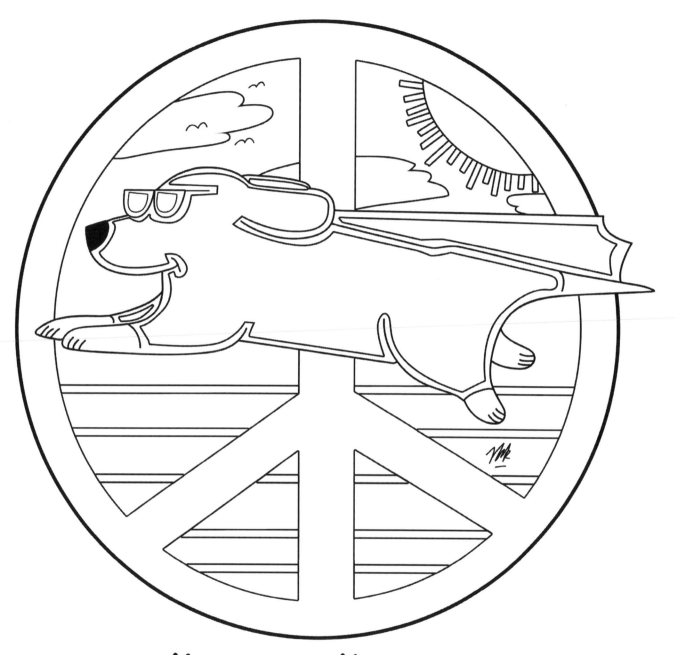

Peace 🐾 **Love** 🐾 **Adopt a Dog**

Burke Brothers Hardware

Supports Homeless Pets!

Family-Owned since 1936

(919) 851-1211

www.burkebrothershardware.com

Acknowledgments From The Artists

Rick

A very special thanks to these amazing people who help make Binky and Bell and this book possible:

Book cover design / graphics design: Eilish Boyd

Editorial review: Kris Ammerman

My family: Paula, Daniel, Sarah, and Nathan

A big thanks goes out to Burke Brothers Hardware in Raleigh, NC. Their help and support of this project were crucial.

The Binky and Bell team: Mark Bell, Kenny Purcell, Eilish Boyd, Kris Ammerman, Cathy Boytos, Donald Antoncich, Janice Adams, Kerry Ahrend, Chris Boudreaux, Joe and Risë McNemar, Karen McElroy, Dan Good, Doug Sadler, Jan Fawley, Kathy Bolton, and Larry Gardner.

Eilish

Thank you to everyone who made this book a reality:

My husband Eric and our pup Piper

My parents and grandparents

My art teachers and mentors: Mary Pat George, Steve Swartwood, Becky Keck and the team at SMARTS community art school, and Kim DeKay

My friend and fellow artist, Rick Gardner, and the Binky and Bell team.

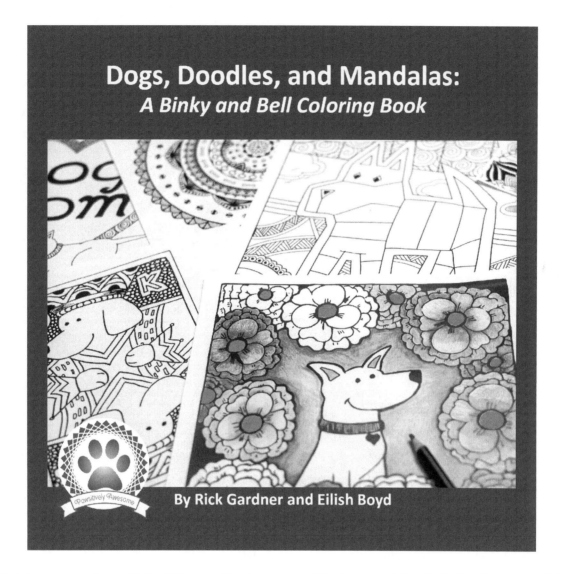

Did you enjoy *This Mutts Be Love: a Binky and Bell Coloring Book*?

Check out the first coloring book by Binky and Bell; Dogs, Doodles, and Mandalas for even more coloring fun!

Order now on www.binkyandbell.com or on amazon.com by searching "Binky and Bell."

THE NAUGHTY DOG JOKE BOOK

The Ultimate Collection of Dad Jokes, Puns, and Cartoon Dog Art

by Binky and Bell

Do you love to laugh? Do you love dogs? Do you need a gift for the dad who has it all?

Check out the first book by Binky and Bell, "The Naughty Dog Joke Book, The Ultimate Collection of Dad Jokes, Puns, and Cartoon Dog Art." Your purchase supports 10 North Carolina dog rescues!

What people are saying:

> "I have enjoyed picking it up over and over and reading whatever is in front of my face. My reactions have ranged from groans to giggles to full-out belly laughs."

> "The artwork is wonderful and the jokes are 100% dad jokes. LOL. We are going to start giving this as a shower gift to all the new dads we know. I love that the proceeds help shelter animals also."

Order now on www.binkyandbell.com or on amazon.com by searching "Binky and Bell."